Reindeer's Red Nose

Sticker & Activity Fun

Santa's Stable

Christmas is drawing near and Santa's reindeer are reporting for duty.
Can you spot seven differences between the two pictures of Santa's stable.

Answers on page 16

Reindeer Friends

A new class are enrolling at Santa's stables and Rosie the Reindeer is the last one to arrive. Follow the clues and help Rosie find her new classmates.

Rosie the Reindeer

CLUES

1. Ralph is the reindeer with a red collar, black nose and is wearing a green saddle cloth.

2. Wendell is the reindeer with a blue collar, black nose and is wearing a green saddle cloth.

3. Suzie is the reindeer with a green collar, brown nose and is wearing a red saddle cloth.

4. Joey is the reindeer with a blue collar, black nose and is wearing a red saddle cloth.

5. Rupert is the reindeer with a green collar, brown nose and is wearing yellow saddle cloth.

Answers on page 16

Reindeer School

Santa's reindeer school is very popular and lots of animals try to get in. Can you work out the one recruit who will get in? Also, can you spot the odd recruit out?

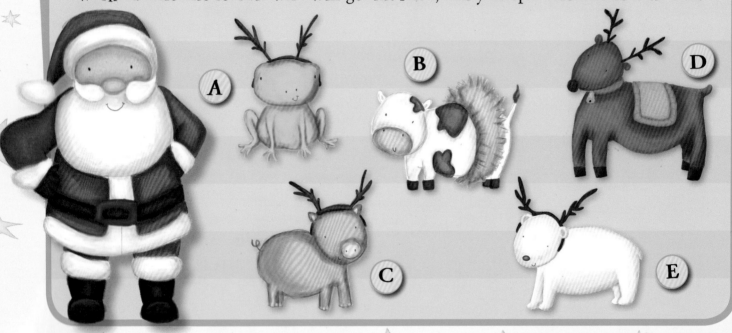

A **B** **D** **C** **E**

Sleigh Repair

Rosie has been asked to help Santa and his elves fix the sleigh. Complete the jigsaw puzzle below. Which piece isn't part of the puzzle?

A **B** **C** **D**

Answers on page 16

Tissue-Paper Trees

Follow the steps below to make your bright tissue-paper tree picture.

You will need:

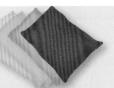

thick card   pencil   scissors   tissue paper   craft glue

1 Use a pencil and draw the outline of a Christmas tree on the thick card. Leave a gap below the tree and draw a pot shape. Also, around the tree draw a present in each corner.

Ask and adult to cut out the tree, pot and present shapes without cutting in from the edge. You will have six holes in your card.

2

Top Tip

Make sure the gaps between cut-out shapes are big enough for you to glue the tissue paper.

Spread glue around the tree-shaped hole and cut a piece of green tissue paper big enough to place over the hole.

3

4

Pick a different shade of tissue paper for each hole and repeat step 3.

5

After the glue is dry, use sticky tack to stick your picture to a window, make sure the tissue-paper side faces the window.

Daydream Drawing

Rosie is daydreaming about pulling Santa's sleigh on Christmas Eve Night.
Draw a picture of Rosie pulling Santa's sleigh.

How to draw a reindeer

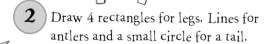

1 Draw a small circle for the head and a large oval for the body.

2 Draw 4 rectangles for legs. Lines for antlers and a small circle for a tail.

3 Add finer detail to the legs and body. Then add a nose and a smiling face.

Woodland Wanders

Rosie and her new friends have gone for a stroll in the woods and have forgotten the way back. Can you help them get back to the stables?

START

END

You will need:
2-4 players
a dice, coins
for counters.

Reindeer Racing

You strain an antler. Miss a turn.

4

2

1

Start

Finish

22

21

Get hit by a snowball. Go back one space

19

8

Reindeer Rooftop Scene

1 Press out all the pieces of your rooftop scene. On the sky background, push out the tab so it sits behind and supports the background card.

2 Slide each tab into the matching slot, then fold forward and stick. Finally, slot piece E into the four slots on pieces A and B. This will support your reindeer.

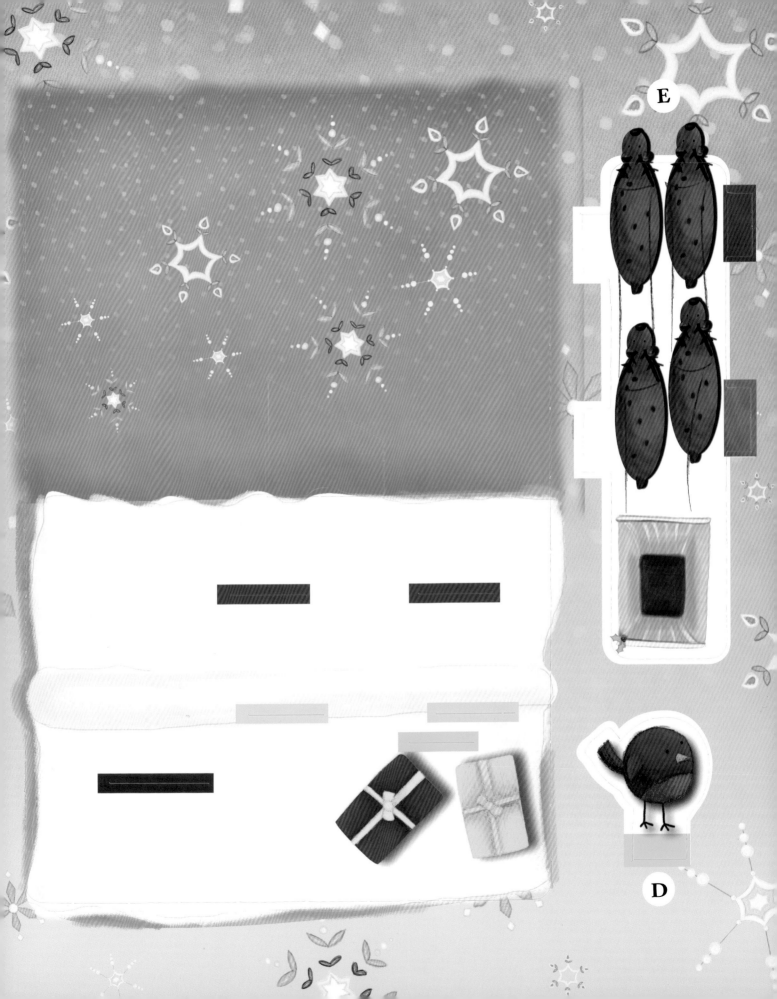

How to play

Place your counters on the start square. Take turns to roll the dice and move your counter the number rolled. If your counter lands on an action square, read and follow the instructions. You must roll the exact number to land on the finish. The first player to the finish square wins the Reindeer Racing!

Slip on the ice. Move forward two spaces.

7

8

Make a wong turn. Go back one space.

10

11

12

Get a burst of energy. Move forward three spaces

14

Have a chat with Santa. Miss a turn.

16

17

Tummy Troubles

Christmas Eve is nearly here, but some of Santa's reindeer aren't feeling well.
Match the patterns on the get-well gifts to the sick reindeer beds.

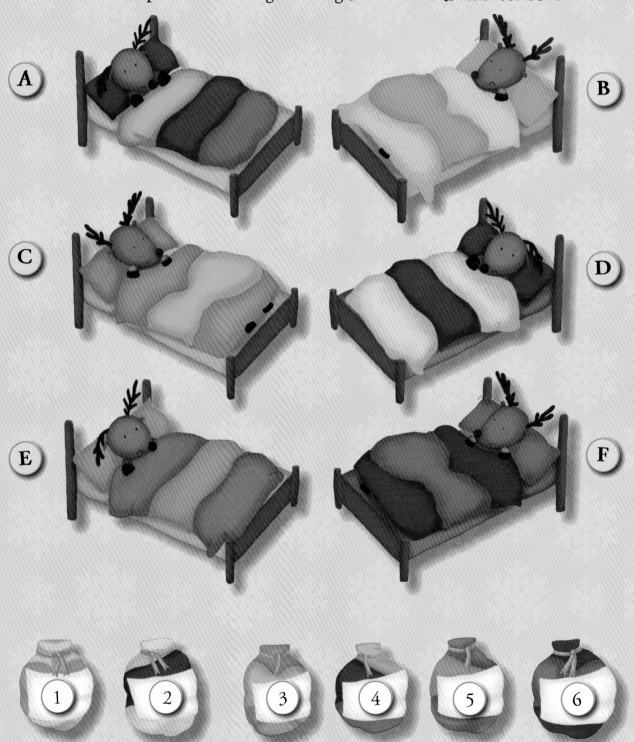

Rosie Remembers

Rosie wants to be the best in class, but she needs your help. Look at the picture below and remember as much as you can then turn over to answer the questions.

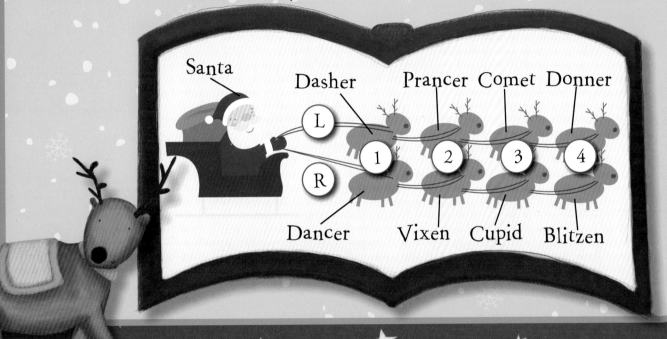

Santa · Dasher · Prancer · Comet · Donner
L · R · 1 · 2 · 3 · 4
Dancer · Vixen · Cupid · Blitzen

Antler Antics

Somebody at the stables has been eating some of the special feed.
Match the shadow clue with one of the possible culprits.

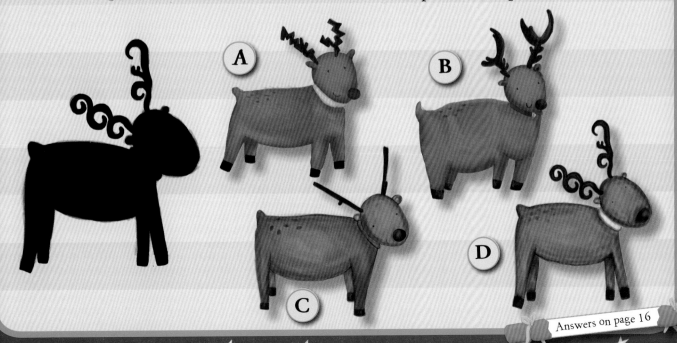

A · B · C · D

Answers on page 16

Rosie Remembers Quiz

You have studied the Christmas text book for 20 seconds,
now answer the questions below.

1. Who is Blitzen's partner?

2. Which row are Comet and Cupid in?

3. Is Vixen on the left or right side of the row?

4. How many reindeer are there in total?

Rosie's Friend

Rosie has caught the feed stealer and has made a new friend.
Connect the dots and discover who's Rosies new friend.

Answers on page 16

Dress Rehearsal

Santa is preparing his reindeer for the big day. Study the picture below and answer the questions at the bottom of the page.

Answers on page 16

1. How many reindeer can you spot?

2. How many elves have beards?

3. How many antlers can you count?

Sleigh in the Balance

Help Santa order his team of reindeer so each pairing is the same weight. Each pair needs to equal 16. Can you spot the reindeer who isn't going with Santa?

Cupid 11

Dancer 10

Donner 9

Blitzen 5

Prancer 6

Dasher 8

Comet 7

Vixen 12

Rosie 4

REINDEER		REINDEER		
		+		= 16
		+		= 16
		+		= 16
		+		= 16

Answers on page 16

Rooftop Rosie

Rosie is at the front of Santa's sleigh and wants to remember the special moment forever. Copy the picture square by square in the grid below.

Answers

Page 2: Santa's Stable

Page 3: Reindeer Friends

Ralph=F, Wendell=A, Suzie=C, Joey=G, Rupert=E

Page 4: Reindeer School

D will get into the reindeer school. B doesn't have any antlers and is the odd one out.

Page 4: Sleigh Repair

Pieces A, B and C complete the puzzle. Piece D is the odd one out.

Page 7: Woodland Wanders

Page 10: Tummy Troubles

A=4, B=1, C=3, D=2, E=5, F=6

Page 11: Antler Antics

The culprit is reindeer D.

Page 12: Rosie Remembers Quiz

1. Donner
2. Row 3
3. Right side
4. There are 8 reindeer.

Page 12: Rosie's Friend

Page 13: Dress Rehearsal

1. There are 16 reindeer
2. Four elves have beards
3. There are 32 antlers.

Page 14: Sleigh in the Balance

Dancer + Prancer
Donner + Comet
Cupid + Blitzan
Vixen + Rosie

Dasher doesn't help Santa this Christmas.